GREYFRIARS BOBBY

The classic story of the Most famous dog in Scotland

Richard Brassey

Orion
Children's Books

First published in Great Britain in 2000
by Orion Children's Books
a division of the Orion Publishing Group Ltd
Orion House, 5 Upper St Martin's Lane, London WC2H 9EA
An Hachette UK company
Reissued 2010

A catalogue record for this book is available from the British Library.

Printed in China

Greyfriars Bobby is the most famous dog who ever lived in Scotland.

He was so famous that a statue was put up to him in Edinburgh.

He was born about a hundred and fifty years ago, but nobody knows where.
Some people say the Highlands.
Some say Skye.
Some say he was born in the Pentland Hills where his master
was a shepherd.
This is nonsense.

We know that Bobby belonged to an Edinburgh policeman named John Gray. He was a Skye Terrier and his job was to bite the ankles of escaping criminals. Bobby was good at that.

But one bitterly cold winter John Gray fell ill with a terrible fever.
Bobby snuggled close to him to try and keep him warm.

He stayed beside his master even when John Gray died.

He followed the funeral procession to Greyfriars churchyard.

NO DOG

Bobby stayed on after the last mourner went home.
He watched as the grave was filled in. He stood on the
bare earth and howled. When night came he
crept under a gravestone to keep guard.

The days came and went, and still Bobby refused to leave his master's grave.

Dogs were not really allowed in the churchyard, but James Brown, the gardener, felt sorry for Bobby and let him stay. On cold nights he even invited him in. But Bobby would never desert his master for long.

When spring came, Bobby chased away all the cats in the churchyard. Mr Brown was pleased.

The cats had been a nuisance.

Bobby soon made plenty of other friends. There were the poor
people, whose crowded houses backed on to the churchyard . . .
the boys of Heriot's School, who climbed over the wall . . .

the owners of all the nearby eating houses . . . and a soldier who used to take him up to the castle to see the gun, which was fired off every day at one o'clock.

Bobby soon got into the habit of setting off for dinner at the sound of the one o'clock gun. People gathered each day to see him trotting past. The story of the faithful dog had spread all over Edinburgh.

One day a new owner arrived at Bobby's favourite restaurant. Mr Traill was not from Edinburgh and had never heard of Bobby, but he realised that many people paid to eat there just to see him.

HIS MASTER WAS A SHEPHERD. HE DIED IN MY ARMS.

I'VE KNOWN HIM SINCE HE WAS A PUPPY.

He gave Bobby lots of extra tasty food, to make sure he came every day. He even made up stories about Bobby for anyone who asked.

But Mr Traill was not so keen when he was ordered to appear in court to explain why he hadn't paid Bobby's dog licence.

HE'S NO MY DOG, YOUR HONOUR. HE STILL BELONGS TO HIS DEAD MASTER.

ARE YOU SUGGESTING WE DIG UP HIS MASTER AND ASK **HIM** FOR THE MONEY?

The most important person in Edinburgh was the Lord Provost. When he heard the story, he was touched by Bobby's faithfulness.

He announced that he would pay Bobby's licence for life. He gave him a special collar with a brass plate.

GREYFRIARS BOBBY
FROM THE LORD PROVOST
1867 Licensed

The story was reported in all the newspapers. Greyfriars was soon crowded with sightseers, painters and photographers.

It's even rumoured that Bobby had a visit from Queen Victoria and her servant, John Brown.

A lot of nonsense has been talked about Bobby over the years.

Some people said he never existed just because they couldn't find him when they visited the churchyard.

Others, who wouldn't have known a Skye Terrier from a poodle, pronounced that Bobby was a Scotty.

Some people just wanted to make a name for themselves.

I WAS HIS FRIEND WHEN HE HAD'NA A FRIEND IN THE WORLD!

A journalist made headlines by claiming he had invented the whole story after a vicious dog chased him from the churchyard . . .

and Mr Traill went on making up stories about Bobby until his dying day.

It's not surprising that when an American lady decided to write a book about Bobby she got many things wrong. It didn't help either that she had never been to Scotland and made most of it up. But the book was very popular and years later Walt Disney made a film based on it.

Whatever people may say about Bobby, we know enough to be sure that he did exist.

At Huntly House Museum in Edinburgh you'll find his collar, his bowl and a real photo of him, looking rather old and sad. You'll even find a photo of Mr Traill and his family with Bobby.

Bobby spent fourteen years faithfully guarding his master's grave. When he died, he was buried in a flowerpot in front of Greyfriars church. A hundred years later, a stone was put up to mark the spot.

Even today there are people who say they see him, chasing cats in the churchyard.

Contents

Some words are printed in bold, **like this**. You can find out what they mean by looking in the glossary.

What are rainforests like?

Forests are places where trees are the main type of plant. A rainforest is a forest that gets a lot of rain. Some rainforests are warm and some are cool.

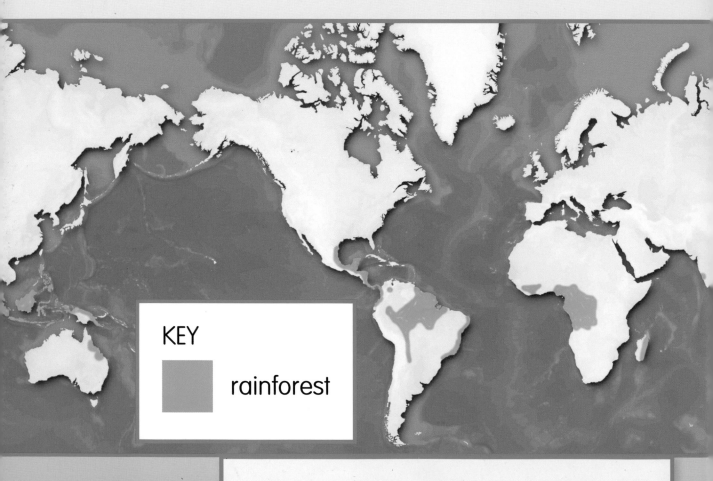

KEY

rainforest

Tropical rainforests are found in places where the weather is always warm.

Rainforests are thick forests with tall trees and many other plants.

The animals in this book live in **tropical** rainforests. Tropical rainforests are warm all the year round. Rainforests are full of food – so they are full of life!

Living in a rainforest

Monkeys, parrots, and many other animals live in rainforests. Some live high in the trees. Others live on the ground. All rainforest animals must **survive** in a hot, wet **environment**.

Lemurs spend most of their time up in the trees.

This butterfly's wings are brown underneath. Lifting up its wings can help it hide from birds.

Rainforest animals have special **features** that help them survive in their surroundings. These features are called **adaptations**.

What is camouflage?

Camouflage is an **adaptation** that helps animals to hide. The colour of an animal's skin, fur, or feathers may match the things around it.

A jaguar's spots help it to hide in the rainforest.

Caimans are related to alligators. This caiman looks like part of a log!

Animals that eat other animals are called **predators**. Camouflage makes it easier for them to hide. This helps them catch food.

Animals that **predators** eat are called **prey** animals. **Camouflage** helps them, too. A prey animal hides so it will not become a predator's meal!

What makes this chameleon blend in so well with the leaves around it?

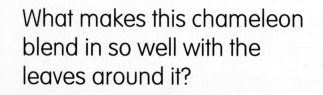

Find the rainforest animals

Three-toed sloth

Some types of three-toed sloths live high in rainforest trees. Can you see how the colour of their fur helps them to **blend in**?

CAMOUFLAGED

Sloths move very slowly. They cannot run from danger. Their fur helps them to hide from **predators**, such as jaguars.

REVEALED

Leafy katydid

When is a leaf not a leaf? When it is a leafy katydid! Animals such as bats, birds, lizards, and spiders eat katydids. A katydid's colours help it to hide from them.

CAMOUFLAGED

Some katydids are green, like leaves. Some are brown, like tree **bark**. They are active at night. During the day, katydids stay very still so they are hard to spot.

Horned frog

Horned frogs live on the forest floor. They have two points on their heads. The frogs' colours and shape make them look like dead leaves.

CAMOUFLAGED

Horned frogs use **camouflage** when they catch food. A frog stays very still until **prey** passes by. Then the frog shoots out its sticky tongue and gobbles up the prey!

REVEALED

Leaf-tailed gecko

A leaf-tailed gecko can flatten its body against a tree. Its tail is shaped like a leaf. This lets the gecko hide while it sleeps.

The tail helps the gecko in another way, too. If a **predator** grabs a gecko's tail, the tail drops off. This lets the gecko escape! Then the gecko grows a new tail.

REVEALED

Imperial moth

The imperial moth has a clever way of hiding in a rainforest. It looks just like a leaf! When it stays still, it disappears amongst the leaves on the forest floor.

An imperial moth does not eat when it is an adult. Other animals might try to eat it, though! The moth's shape and colour help it to hide from hungry animals.

REVEALED

CAMOUFLAGED

Great potoo

Potoo birds hunt at night and sleep during the day. Potoos have feathers that look like tree **bark**. This helps the sleeping birds stay safe.

If danger comes near, potoos close their eyes. They point their beaks up to the sky. This makes the potoos look even more like pieces of a tree!

Reticulated python

Reticulated pythons are the world's longest snakes. They can be over 9 metres long! Can you see how the python's skin **pattern** helps it **blend in**?

CAMOUFLAGED

Sometimes a python hunts by hiding in a tree. Its **camouflage** helps it hide. When **prey** passes below, the python catches it. Then it swallows the prey whole.

Orchid mantis

The orchid mantis looks like a flower! Its legs are shaped like petals. It is very hard to spot a mantis on a plant.

CAMOUFLAGED

The orchid mantis eats other insects. It sits and waits for **prey** to pass by. Then the mantis grabs the prey with its front legs.

REVEALED

This owl monkey's fur helps it hide in rainforest trees.

The rainforest is full of **camouflaged** animals. If you are ever lucky enough to visit a rainforest, look closely. You never know what you might see!

Animals that stand out

Some types of birds of paradise live on the island of New Guinea. There are few large **predators** on the island. So the birds do not need to hide.

Male birds of paradise have bright colours that help them attract mates.

The blue poison arrow frog stands out in the rainforest.

Poison arrow frogs have **poisons** in their skin. Their bright colours warn animals not to eat them. The frogs come in many colours. Some are red with blue legs. They are called blue jeans frogs!

29

Glossary

adaptation special feature that helps an animal survive in its surroundings

bark tough, outer part of a tree trunk

blend in matches well with the things around it

camouflage adaptation that helps an animal blend in with its surroundings

environment place where an animal lives

feature special part of an animal

pattern shapes and marks on an animals skin, fur, or feathers

poison something dangerous that can make you very ill, or even kill you

predator animal that eats other animals

prey animal that other animals eat

survive stay alive

tropical place that is very warm all the year round

Find out more

Books to read

Animals: A Children's Encyclopedia
  (Dorling Kindersley, 2008)

Essential Habitats: Tropical Rainforest Habitats,
  Barbara Taylor (TickTock Media Ltd., 2009)

Focus on Habitats: Rainforest Animals,
  Stephen Savage (Wayland, 2006)

Websites

**www.bbc.co.uk/nature/habitats/Tropical_and_
subtropical_moist_broadleaf_forests**
A BBC website where you can watch films and find
out more about your favourite rainforest animals.

www.nhm.ac.uk/kids-only/life/life-jungle
Discover more fascinating facts about rainforests on
the Natural History Museum's Kids Only website.

Index